A MIRACLE IN THE KITCHEN

A Legend about Saint Zita

Written by Pamela Love

Illustrated by Sheila Bailey

Pauline
BOOKS & MEDIA
Boston

Library of Congress Control Number: 2020934600
CIP data is available.

ISBN-10: 0-8198-0872-5
ISBN-13: 978-0-8198-0872-1

Illustrated by Sheila Bailey

Design by Daughters of St. Paul

"P" and PAULINE are registered trademarks of the Daughters of St. Paul.

Published by Pauline Books & Media, 50 Saint Paul's Avenue, Boston, MA 02130-3491

Printed in Korea.

AMITK SIPSKOGUNKYO12-13085 0872-5

www.pauline.org

Pauline Books & Media is the publishing house of the Daughters of St. Paul, an international congregation of women religious serving the Church with the communications media.

1 2 3 4 5 6 7 8 9   26 25 24 23 22

To all who help
those in need.

Long ago in Italy, a girl named Zita stirred coals in a fireplace until they glowed hot. Glancing outside at the rising sun, she thought, *I must hurry! If everything is not ready by the time the cook wakes up, I will be in trouble.*

Zita was twelve. She was a maid for the rich Fatinelli family in the city of Lucca. All day, it was work and more work, from lighting the fireplaces before breakfast until washing the supper dishes at night. In between came milking cows, gathering eggs, bringing in water, cleaning the house, and on and on. She was the first person up in the morning and the last one in bed at night. Sometimes she thought she would need wings to move fast enough to do everything that was expected of her.

3

The rudeness of the other servants made Zita's job even harder. The cook was especially harsh. "Scrub the floor! Bring firewood! Get water! Hurry up!" She never gave Zita a chance to do anything before yelling.

Zita could not quit. Good jobs were hard to find. At least here, she had enough to eat. Signor Fatinelli told all the servants, "Work hard or I will fire you and hire someone else!"

Busy as she was, every morning before dawn, Zita tiptoed out the door. Hurrying through the streets, she often whispered, "Lord, please help me get to Mass on time. Then help me get home to finish my morning's work before the cook wakes up."

Zita's only friends were people from church. They were poor, too. Many were servants like she was.

"It was so different in the village where I grew up," Zita told her friend, Anna. "I wish I could visit my family, but I do not have the time or money to go see them." She remembered their loving goodbyes when she had moved away to find work. She knew her parents wished they could have supported her until she was older, but they were too poor.

"My family lives here in the city, but I can only see them at Mass. We are all so busy," said Anna.

Zita nodded and hugged her friend. "God will give us the strength we need."

On the rare days when she had free time, Zita helped Anna's family with cooking and cleaning. Their sincere thanks made her happier than money could.

When the Fatinellis' cook found out, she was furious. "Wasting time working somewhere else?! We need a maid in this house, not an angel!"

"But I only help them after I have finished my chores," Zita said.

"Bad enough you go to church every day. You have too little to do," sneered the cook. "You will do some of my work."

The cook had Zita bake the bread each day. It was a big job. First, she heated the oven. Then, she mixed flour, water, and yeast into dough. With her hands, she formed the loaves. The yeast made them rise, but that took time. While she waited for them to be ready, Zita did her other chores.

She was busier and more tired than ever. "Lord, help me remember that in serving this family, I am serving you. Please let me continue working here, praying, and helping those in need," Zita prayed. At least she still found comfort in going to Mass every morning.

One Sunday, Zita did not see Anna or Anna's family in church.

"Anna's mother is sick," her neighbor said. "And Anna is too busy working to help her."

Stopping by their home after church, Zita found Anna's mother in bed with a fever. The other children were too young to help. "I will return when I can," Zita promised her.

Zita dashed to the Fatinellis' house. She was supposed to have Sunday afternoons off, although the cook almost never allowed it. "This afternoon, may I please go help some friends?"

The cook shook her head. "No. You need to bake the bread for dinner tonight, lazy girl."

Zita pleaded, "But my friend's mother is sick, and I promised to help her."

"If you want to work, do it here. If that bread is not baked, you will be fired."

As Zita washed the dishes, she prayed, "Lord, my friends need me. But if I lose my job, I might not find another. Please help me know what to do."

By the time Zita put away the last plate, she had decided. *I will go help my friend's family. When I get back, I will make the bread.*

Noticing that Zita was not in the kitchen, the cook muttered to herself, "Zita thinks she is so much better than the rest of us. Just wait until the Fatinellis find out she has left without making the bread!"

After the noontime meal, the cook said to Signor and Signora Fatinelli, "There is a problem in the kitchen. Please let me show you."

Curious, her employers followed her. "Is there trouble with the oven?" asked Signora Fatinelli, as she walked to the kitchen. Opening the door for them, the cook snickered. She knew they would be furious when they saw Zita was not at work.

The Fatinellis gasped and sank to their knees.

"What is going on?" the cook asked, standing in the doorway.

There in the dark kitchen an angel was kneading the dough! Smiling, the angel made one loaf after another.

When Zita returned, she paused on the doorstep. "Lord, I am glad I helped Anna's family. Now, God, help me accept the consequences of my choice. Amen."

The cook opened the door. "Zita!" she shouted, but she was not angry. Ashamed, she looked down. "I am sorry I was unkind to you. I was wrong. But now, come! Hurry!" She ran down the hall.

Zita followed the cook to the kitchen. There, the
Fatinellis were kneeling in prayer. The angel opened
the oven and slid out the bread. Zita prayed out loud,
"Lord, thank you for your kindness in sending me help."

About Saint Zita of Italy

Saint Zita of Italy (who is also called Saint Zita of Lucca) was born in 1212, in a village called Monte Sagrati. She worked for the Fatinelli family for almost fifty years.

Following Zita's example, the Fatinellis began going to Mass regularly. When Zita grew up, they promoted her so that she was in charge of the other servants. She also took care of the Fatinelli children. She was glad to do this work, and thought it was an important way to serve the Lord.

Zita kept on bringing food and help to the sick and poor all of her life. She also visited people in jail.

Saint Zita died in 1272. Her body lies in the Basilica di San Frediano, where she often went to worship. Her feast day is April 27. She is the patron saint of domestic servants, restaurant servers, and the city of Lucca.

Prayer to Saint Zita

Saint Zita, you always found time to worship God, no matter how busy you were with your work and helping others. I want to be faithful, too. Please help me to do all that I need to do, including schoolwork, chores, and, most importantly, praying to God. Amen.

Pamela Love

After growing up in New Jersey, Pamela Love attended Bucknell University. She worked as a teacher and in marketing before turning to writing. She is the author of numerous picture books and has written many stories and poems for children's magazines. Pamela is the author of *Brigid and the Butter: A Legend about Saint Brigid of Ireland, Staircase for the Sisters: A Story about Prayer and Saint Joseph, The Sword and the Cape: A Tale of Saint Martin of Tours,* and *A Prayer and a Pickaxe: A Legend about Saint Clement of Rome.* She is also a contributor to *Family Matters: Thirteen Short Stories,* all published by Pauline Books & Media. She and her family live in Maryland.

Sheila Bailey

Sheila Bailey is freelance illustrator with over three decades of experience. Clients have included Scholastic, Harper Collins, Golden Books, and Pelican Press. She currently lives on Sauvie Island, Oregon. You can see more of her work at sheilabaileyart.com.

SMILE
God Loves You!

Who are the Daughters of St. Paul?

We are Catholic sisters. Our mission is to be like Saint Paul and tell everyone about Jesus! There are so many ways for people to communicate with each other. We want to use all of them so everyone will know how much God loves us. We do this by printing books (you're holding one!), making radio shows, singing, helping people at our bookstores, using the internet, and in many other ways.

VISIT OUR WEB SITE AT WWW.PAULINE.ORG

BOOKS & MEDIA

The Daughters of St. Paul operate book and media centers at the following addresses. Visit, call, or write the one nearest you today, or find us at www.paulinestore.org.

CALIFORNIA
3908 Sepulveda Blvd, Culver City, CA 90230   310-397-8676
3250 Middlefield Road, Menlo Park, CA 94025   650-562-7060

FLORIDA
145 S.W. 107th Avenue, Miami, FL 33174   305-559-6715

HAWAII
1143 Bishop Street, Honolulu, HI 96813   808-521-2731

ILLINOIS
172 North Michigan Avenue, Chicago, IL 60601   312-346-4228

LOUISIANA
4403 Veterans Memorial Blvd, Metairie, LA 70006   504-887-7631

MASSACHUSETTS
885 Providence Hwy, Dedham, MA 02026   781-326-5385

MISSOURI
9804 Watson Road, St. Louis, MO 63126   314-965-3512

NEW YORK
115 E. 29th Street, New York City, NY 10016   212-754-1110

SOUTH CAROLINA
243 King Street, Charleston, SC 29401   843-577-0175

VIRGINIA
1025 King Street, Alexandria, VA 22314   703-549-3806

CANADA
3022 Dufferin Street, Toronto, ON M6B 3T5   416-781-9131

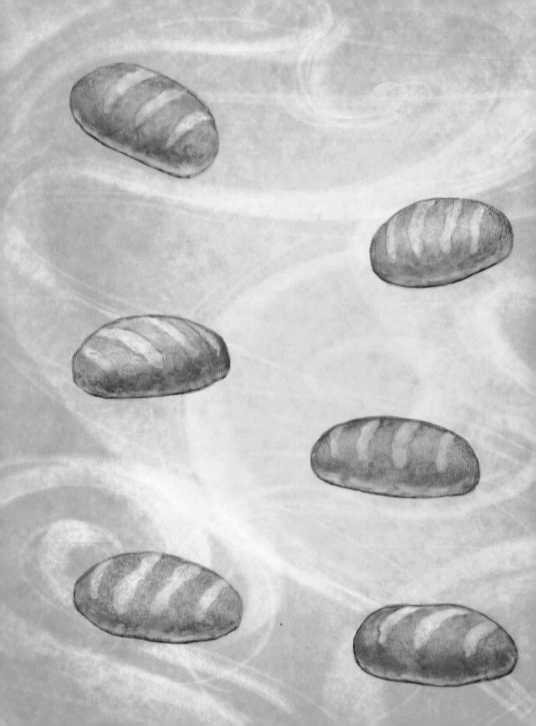